FIRE MOUNTAIN

The Eruptions of Mount St. Helens

Volcanoes keep a primal hold on our imagination. They're so unlike the good earth, terra firma, that solid and domestic glebe and ground upon which we so confidently tread from day to day. Volcanoes are the earth come to passionate life. The very name summons up our hoariest myths. Ugly, soot-streaked Vulcan, cast out from the heavenly salon, is at work again. His subterranean forges and smoky bellows are busy fashioning a cunning trap with which to ensnare his surpassingly beautiful and faithless wife. Volcanoes excite our curiosity – always have – with their billowing contrails of ash and fiery rivers of lava. Pliny the Elder, the very pattern of the natural scientist, lost his life on the flanks of Vesuvius.

Between eruptions, though, we forget where we are. Living beside silent peaks for some centuries, we suppose this a constant state of affairs. By its very slowness, monumental geologic process becomes invisible to us. Blissfully unaware or disbelieving, we float away our lives atop a mantle of molten rock. Then, one day, the mountain awakes, shakes forth a spark of the divine fire, and we remember everything.

James Mason

Captain George Vancouver
1757-1798
Courtesy of the Oregon Historical Society

Alleyne Fitzherbert Baron St. Helens, confirmed bachelor and career diplomat, never saw the mountain which bears his name. Mount St. Helens, we call it, this volcano with a terrible temper that rises in the Cascade range of the Pacific Northwest. In fact, although widely traveled (he served as England's envoy to the court of Empress Catherine of Russia) St. Helens never even set foot in the Americas. That rough work was left to people like Captain George Vancouver, who, from the deck of his ship at the mouth of the Columbia River in May of 1792, spied a symmetrical white peak glimmering in the distance.

How exasperating! In this latitude the mountains kept popping up like toadstools. First Mount Baker, then Mount Rainier and now a third one. Very well.

Indefatigable Vancouver knew beyond shirking that the duty of the European explorer in the new world—like Adam's in Eden—was to dispense names. His logic in honoring St. Helens isn't recorded, but may have gone something like this: St. Helens had recently negotiated a favorable treaty with Spain over control of the Northwest coast of the continent. He was a protégé of the king (whom it didn't hurt to please.)

And third—who knows?—it may even have occurred to Vancouver that in important ways the mountain resembled the man. St. Helens the diplomat had a reputation for consummate prudence and a quiet, polished manner. The mountain that day, with its gracefully rounded slopes and smooth mantle of snow, was certainly a visual ambassador of the area, putting the western shore's best aesthetic foot forward. Looking at the peak from the Columbia estuary, Vancouver would have had no reason to doubt it was as benign as Mont Blanc, (but not so large) a durable memorial to the virtues of moderation. In any event, Captain Vancouver made his decision: henceforth, the mountain would be known as St. Helens, and so it has remained ever since.

In most circles. The natives didn't necessarily go along. Vancouver notwithstanding, the Klickitat Indians continued to call the mountain by its traditional name–Tahonelatclah. In so doing, they had the advantage over the Englishman of having lived alongside it for several thousand years. These days, the rest of us are beginning to understand the wisdom of the Klickitats' choice–for translated from their native tongue, Tahonelatclah means Fire Mountain.

Fire Mountain indeed. Almost 188 years to the day of its christening, undiplomatic Mount St. Helens let loose a lateral blast of hot ash and gas that literally blew away a forest of giant Douglas Fir and 13 percent of its top. The explosion, one of the largest volcanic eruptions in the world this century, radically altered the terrain around the mountain–from thickly vegetated to scorched and bare. It also altered the psychological landscape for millions of Pacific Northwest residents. All those beautiful Cascade peaks that run like a mighty backbone from the Canadian border down to northern California aren't just occasions for postcards people stopped to think–they're volcanoes. And volcanoes erupt.

Many Indian legends warned of the dangers around Fire Mountain. According to these stories, Spirit Lake at its base was a forlorn, haunted place. Man-eating fish with heads like bears lived there, as did the phantasmagorical Seatco–a clan of dead souls cast out from their tribes because of their wickedness. On still nights, it was said, the sound of a ghost waterfall could be heard tumbling under the Lake's surface.

Canadian artist Paul Kane was on a tour of the West, sketching scenes of Indians and wildlife, when he witnessed several of Mount St. Helen's 19th century eruptions. While highly romanticized, Kane's painting does accurately place the volcano's vent on the mountain's northwest side, about a third the way down its flank. The painting's setting is from the mouth of the Lewis River. Kane wanted to get closer, but the fear of Indian guides–of a lake full of strange bear-fish and evil spirits that ate men–was too great. "I offered a considerable bribe to any Indian who would accompany me in St. Helens exploration," Kane noted in his journal of March 26, 1847, "but could not find one hardy enough to venture."

In the Klickitat creation story, Fire Mountain is personified as a lovely Indian maiden, Loowit, who coquettishly provokes two young warriors, Wyeast (Mount Hood) and Klickitat (Mount Adams) into a fire and brimstone battle for her favor. But Loowit wasn't always the irresistable vamp, the legend explains. She had once been a toothless old crone who got the chance to do an important favor for the Great Spirit. In return, the Great Spirit asked her what she wanted. Loowit's wish was to be changed back into a young and beautiful woman.

Commentators have suggested that this myth embodies a kind of folk history of the repeated physical changes the Klickitats would have observed taking place on the mountain over the centuries. The mountain probably waxed and waned in size from eruption to eruption. What looked like a low-lying heap of smoking black lava one century would have – after successive layers of pumice and lava built it up – metamorphosed into a snow-enshrouded, idealized beauty the next. It was this aspect of the changing mountain that white settlers first encountered.

The newcomers would see the volcano in action soon enough, however. From 1831 to 1857 St. Helens erupted periodically and the journals of the times are replete with references to this "grand and sublime spectacle." On occasion, enough ash drifted over the trading post at Vancouver so that "lighted candles were necessary during the day." For the most part, though, the mountain was on the other side of an untracked wilderness, too far away to worry about.

The first expedition to climb the mountain was led by Thomas J. Dryer, editor of the Oregonian, in August of 1853. Of his group's summit experience, Dryer somewhat sourly told his readers: "Each face looked pale and sallow. It appeared as if there were hundreds of fine-toned bells ringing in our ears. Blood started from our noses and all of us found respiration difficult. With this exception we all felt well."

By the turn of the century, following the discovery of copper ore in the vicinity, Cowlitz County built a wagon road to the lake. The ore played out in a few years, but the people didn't. The Mazamas, a Portland mountaineering club, began to stage regular climbs. The YMCA, and later Boy Scouts and Girl Scouts, established permanent campgrounds on the margin of the lake. Gradually, more lodges and cabins went up; the Spirit Lake of so many happy vacation memories was taking shape.

The place had a magnetic appeal. People were drawn to the spectacle of the looming mountain upended and rippling in the cobalt blue water. Around the lake rose massive Doug Fir, hemlock, spruce – old growth trees, thick and tall. The camp kids splashed and yelled in the water each morning – but not for long, the water was as cold as it was crystal clear.

For backpackers, the rosary of lakes in the Mount Margaret back country made an ideal destination. Pan-fried brown trout hit the spot after a trek through the woods. The mountain itself was one of the most popular climbs in the Northwest. 7700 people registered to go up it in 1979. There were trails for horseback riding in the summer, for cross-country skiing in the winter. Fishermen came from around the world to the banks of the Toutle each winter to catch steelhead – an ocean-touring trout that thinks it's a salmon and fights like a lion. In the forest, there were brown bear, deer, one of the state of Washington's largest elk herds.

And loggers. Now that the forest has been leveled, chroniclers have tended to portray it as a place of primeval beauty prior to the volcano's rude outburst. As a matter of fact, whatever the vistas from Spirit Lake, elsewhere the clearcuts on the mountain's flanks ran right up to timberline. Indeed, satellite photographs of the Gifford Pinchot National Forest prior to the blast show, especially to the south and east, large areas wholly stripped of trees. Environmentalists were incensed. They accused the Forest Service of wholesale capitulation to the timber industry, and labeled its management of the Gifford Pinchot "a national disgrace." They tried to get the area turned over to the jurisdiction of the National Park Service.

In retrospect, it was the mountain's very beauty – its perfect arcuate shape covered in snow year round – that fueled the arguments over whether the trees around it should be cut down. This same beauty drew vacationers to it in huge numbers. To geologists, though, all that appealing alpine symmetry bespoke something else: danger.

Climbers on the icefall of Forsyth Glacier (above). Mount St. Helens has always been among the most popular climbs in the Northwest, although it presented few technical problems to the mountaineer.

The reflection of Mount St. Helens glimmers in Spirit Lake (below). For thousands of vacationers each summer, this scene of snow-capped majesty seemed a timeless one. In reality, though, the mountain was geologically younger than the hills around it. Its active volcanism was evidenced by its low timberline. The forest on the north side had been beaten back by pumice avalanches as recently as about the year 1800.

(opposite page) Giant fir trees in the Quartz Creek Natural Area of the Gifford Pinchot National Forest overarched a Douglas squirrel and snow-laden hemlock. Deep soil and great quantities of rain and snow made the land around Mount St. Helens one of the finest timber-growing areas in the world. Outdoor lovers worried that the area was being overexploited, to the detriment of the land and its wild creatures.

Mount St. Helens, a scoop of ice cream alongside the glacially carved up volcanoes near it, looked young for good reason – because it was. The entire visible part of the mountain had been built up since 500 B.C. Even in human terms, that's not very old (the Great Pyramids at Gizeh date back to around 3000 B.C.); in geological terms, it's hardly a tick of the clock. In fact, the volcano was far younger than the green hills that surrounded it. And, like any youngster, geologists realized, St. Helens was still prone to fits.

To be sure, we were warned – not by our poets as were the Klickitats, but by the new bringers of truth – the scientists. In 1975, three members of a U.S. Geological Survey volcano hazards evaluation team published a prediction in Science magazine. Through patient, systematic detective work using carbon dating techniques, they had reconstructed the geologic history of the mountain. What they discovered was that St. Helens was indeed the enfante terrible of the Cascade range. Not only that, it was by far the most active, and explosively dangerous, volcano in the conterminous 48 states. For instance, the geologists charted one eruption that had dumped two feet of yellowish-brown pumice on the sides of Mount Rainier, 50 miles to the north. The lobe of ash could be traced all the way up to Alberta, Canada. In that single episode, the geologists figured, St. Helens had tossed out more material than Vesuvius emitted in burying Pompeii.

Nor was that an anomaly. The stratigraphic record clearly showed that St. Helens had been a regular performer – going off in a big way every 100 years for the past millenium. This fact, coupled with the realization that the mountain hadn't erupted since 1857, led the geologists to a conclusion – which they published in Science: namely, that St. Helens was overdue and would probably soon erupt.

Interestingly enough, one of the authors of this paper, Donal Mullineaux, grew up practically in the shadow of St. Helens – in Camas, Washington. During his field trips each summer, Mullineaux would walk the trails and byways of the Gifford Pinchot forest looking for more clues. As he passed the wood trillium and venus slipper and salal in the deep shade of the big fir, the thought would occasionally come to him that one day the mountain might gather all this back in – as it had before.

The folks in the nearby town of Cougar got to know "those geologist fellers" too. Sometimes Mullineaux and the Cougar shopkeepers would get to talking about the mountain's erratic past; about how a pahoehoe lava flow had once cascaded down the Lewis River valley; about the common instances of pyroclastic flows, pumice emissions and columns of ash in the past; about how the city of Castle Rock, some 40 miles downstream of the Toutle River, was built upon an historic mudflow several feet thick.

The town folk would listen in a dreamy way to all this, then kid Mullineaux about his soft government job – getting paid to camp out around the mountain all summer. The prospect of an eruption seemed something of a fantasy to them. Scientists could beat their drums, but one look at the mountain made the idea hard to credit.

Bob & Ira Spring

© Gary Braasch

Ron Cronin

In the Mount Margaret roadless area to the north of Spirit Lake, a camper meets the forest in all its aboriginal diversity (above). Maidenhair fern luxuriated in the wet, shadowy depths of the Gifford Pinchot (left). At higher altitudes, meadows of Indian Paintbrush were a showy element in the alpine flora (far right). During the winter, the salal might be encased in ice (above right), but in the summer, its berries –used in syrups or dried and ground into flour and stored as cakes–were one of the few things that could entice Indians into the Spirit Lake area. Game biologists estimate that roughly 200 mountain goats (right) were killed in the May 18 blast of the volcano.

There it was, the Fujiyama of America, cold and beautiful, unmoved and unmoving as far back as anyone in town could remember. Volcanoes were for disaster movies or for far-off lands still in the throes of becoming. Volcanoes were <u>not</u> for societies where man's heirarchy over nature had been firmly established. Volcanoes had exotic, faintly pagan-sounding names, like Krakatoa, Pelee, Nyiragongo. Volcanoes were <u>not</u> named after middle-level English diplomats.

There it was, Mount St. Helens, above the lake, immense and mesmerizing, reassuringly the same year after year. The Forest Service even had a little pamphlet explaining the best way to get a picture of the mountain reflected in Spirit Lake – the best time of day, best place to stand, best exposure to use. And a splendid picture it was. Always the same. The Platonic ideal. So perfect you could imagine it staying that way for-ever. Just the way George Vancouver might have, nearly two centuries earlier.

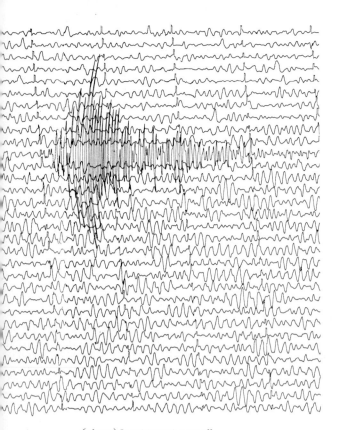

(above) In retrospect, a small, scarcely publicized earthquake on March 20, 1980, was the first harbinger of Mount St. Helens' violent reawakening. Here is how the jolt, 4.1 on the Richter scale, was picked up by the seismograph at Portland State University in downtown Portland. Ironically, the federal listening post closest to the earthquake was shut down for maintenance when the biggest American geological story of the century first surfaced. As a result, the identification of the quake's epicenter as directly beneath the mountain was slightly delayed.

Something trembled under the mountain. The time was precisely 43 seconds after 3:47 p.m. Thursday, March 20, 1980. Seconds later seismometers around the Northwest twitched a response. No one realized it yet, but the eruption of Mount St. Helens was underway.

The National Earthquake Information Center prepared a press release identifying the probable epicenter of the quake as about 18 miles northeast of the mountain. Now, a minor jolt in a rural part of western Washington is not big news. Local papers carried the story on their back pages. In Seattle, the media ran features about an elephant that had learned how to roller skate.

Instead of decaying in intensity, as a tectonic quake normally does, however, day by day the tremors in the vicinity of St. Helens became more and more nervously insistent. And they weren't just in the vicinity. A recalculation of the original jolt's location showed it was right under the mountain. Could the seismographs be recording the bumptious progess of a pool of magma up the throat of the long quiet volcano? Maybe. But the geologists, who had converged on the peak with monitoring equipment, didn't want to sound inflammatory or look silly. They spoke cautiously of the mountain "burping."

Any question of keeping a lid on the story, or the mountain, ended on March 27. On that day, Mike Beard, reporter for a Portland radio station sent up to the mountain in the station's traffic-watch airplane by his news director to "find a fresh angle," did as he was told. "Hey, this thing's exploding!" he radioed back in an excited voice. It was close enough to April Fools Day for Beard's report to meet with some scepticism. But then he began to describe what he saw: a crater-like fissure, maybe 100 feet across, had opened in the top of the mountain. Smoke was pouring out of it "like out of a chimney." Ash was settling in a small black elipse over the pristine snowfield at the top of the mountain.

Officials swung into action: highways leading into the area were blocked off; residents within a ten mile area were ordered out; so were some 300 Weyerhaeuser loggers working in the vicinity. As the mountain continued to perform, sending up ever bigger plumes and enlarging its crater, the media legions descended. Reporters and TV crews from all over the United States, and some from abroad, arrived to cover the action.

In fact, the only thing more surprising than the stygean plumes of steam and ash vented thousands of feet skyward by the born-again volcano was the human reaction to it. Elation.

Brent Wojahn of the Oregonian snuck in via logging roads and avoided highway roadblocks to get this historic photograph of Mount St. Helens (left) reawakening after 123 years of quiet. The plume of steam and ash reaching more than a mile into the sky was the first real eruption in the 1980 volcanic sequence. Wojahn was posted 11 miles to the south, on the flank of Mount Mitchell when it began at 1:48 in the morning of March 28. He shot it at f 2.8 with a 10 second exposure using Tri-X and a nearly full moon.

"It's very small," admitted Harvey Latham, Oregon's chief of emergency services, "but I'm sure it's working up to something good." The mayor of Portland, a city whose entire water supply lies downwind of the volcano, described her overflight of the puffing mountain as "absolutely one of the most beautiful experiences I've ever had."

Her enthusiasm was shared by the public at large. "We want lava, we want lava," went the refrain of a pop tune—one of many—recorded in St. Helen's honor. Best-selling T-shirts took up the theme ("St. Helens is hot!" "Do it, Loowit!") A man "looking for something to do" called the Forest Service requesting clearance to parachute into the crater.

What makes volcanoes tick? The answer is best explained in terms of the theory of plate tectonics (below). According to this theory, the earth's crust, which floats atop the mantle, is divided into twelve plates which are very slowly moving in relation to one another. For instance, the Pacific plate (upon which the Pacific Ocean rests) is bumping into the coast of America as it spreads outward from its center. Since the Pacific plate is much lighter than the massive plates that undergird the continent, it is being forced under the continent. As it is "subducted," tremendous heat and pressure are generated, melting the basaltic oceanic crust and forming a pool of magma. The buoyant magma rises through any available crack. When it reaches the surface, a volcano is born—or as in the case of St. Helens, reawakens.

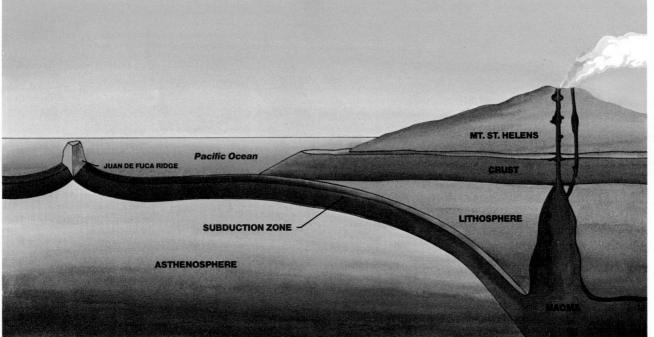

JUAN DE FUCA RIDGE

Pacific Ocean

SUBDUCTION ZONE

ASTHENOSPHERE

MT. ST. HELENS

CRUST

LITHOSPHERE

MAGMA

11

*"I'll do anything for a picture,"
says Ancil Nance, including
climb an active volcano
(below). Two weeks after the
initial eruption, Nance and
two companions skied into the
restricted zone and—under
cover of night to avoid
detection—started the climb to
the crater. They had planned
to make the summit by dawn,
but fell short. Lucky thing, too,
because as day broke, the
mountain erupted in seven or
eight successive blasts. "That
was very impressive," says Pete
Reagan, pictured here. "It just
lobbed 50-60 big rocks up in
the air. That's when I thought,
'well, if one of those landed
on me, it'd kill me.'"*

Although supposedly only scientists and reporters were
allowed to overfly the mountain, by the second day of eruptions 70 planes at a time were jockeying for air space around
the peak, creating one great white blob on the traffic control
radar screen. "It's a real dogfight up there," said a pilot.

A Chicago couple took a commercial jetliner to Portland,
chartered a plane to circle the volcano for an hour, then
immediately flew back home.

On the ground, reporters and sightseers alike got as close
to the mountain as roadblocks would allow. For the time
being, that meant tiny Cougar, Washington. Most frequently
heard question there was, "Where's the mountain?" With
the typically leaden Pacific Northwest skies, it wasn't always
easy to tell. In fact, when the sun was out it wasn't easy to
tell either. You can't see the mountain from Cougar—it's so
close that the foothills block the view. But that didn't seem
to matter to the tourists. They just kept coming.

By Easter Sunday, however, reporters were beginning
to suspect a serious flaw in God's plan for the volcano.

Ancil Nance

*Ash deposits (right) formed a
cement-like bond to the snow
at nighttime that "crampons
would just barely break,"
according to Nance. When the
sun came out, though, the dark
ash absorbed the heat, melting
and forming eerie miniature
versions of the mudflows that
would issue from the peak
months later.*

Ancil Nance

Bob & Ira Spring

An eruption of March 30th (right) as seen from the upper Wind River area looking toward Shoestring Glacier on the mountain's southeast face. The Forest Service plane monitoring the mountain reported "a real beautiful one" in progress. Magically, the clouds opened to give this veiw. Spectators and geologists, many of whom had spent a lifetime studying the Northwest's volcanic past without ever having seen a Cascade peak in action, cheered St. Helens first phreatic puffs. On the following three pages, the plume grows and blows off to the northeast (pictures taken at approximately two minute intervals).

Ron Cronin

In the early eruptions (below), steam rose in billows while the darker ash drifted to the lee, almost like a curtain falling. The result was a Manichaean study in black and white.

As the mountain cleared its throat of old rock and ice, the crater steadily grew in size. By April 11, two large blowholes had virtually knocked out the landbridge separating them to create an immense wound in the mountain–2000 feet in diameter and 500 feet deep. A surveillance helicopter looks as tiny as a caddisfly beside the crater's gaping maw.

Geologists had already briefed them to tears on such humdrum happenings as earthquakes, avalanches, harmonic tremors, mud flows and steam explosions. More of the same wasn't news. So where was the lava?

The Geological Survey responded as best it could. A "geologist of the day" would explain the experiment he was overseeing and its significance in terms of what might happen next. At such a briefing, a young scientist named Dave Johnston told about the Survey's study of the volcano's gaseous emissions. Reporters liked him. He did a good job of translating esoterica into quotable ideas. When the Survey organized an opportunity for reporters to watch the scientists going about their work, it was Johnston who told them while standing at timberline, "If the mountain exploded now,

Ancil Nance

we would die. It's like standing next to a keg of dynamite with the fuse lit – only we don't know how long the fuse is."

That was the problem. Geologists were just the opposite of the weatherman. Their long term predictions were very accurate; from day to day, though, they could forecast very little. But people were eager for news. On nice weekends a thousand or more spectators, cameras at the ready, would line the shore of Yale Lake, just below Cougar waiting for the fireworks to begin. But local residents had already gotten used to the idea of these picturesque bursts coming out of the peak – they wanted back in; and so did the loggers; and so did the fishermen.

Besides, some scientists were beginning to doubt the imminence of a catastrophic event. A Dartmouth team sampled the gases coming out of the crater and found them low in sulfur dioxide – an indicator that the magma was still far down in the volcano's netherworld. Was the evacuation really necessary?

Lining up with the skeptics was the world's foremost charismatic volcanologist, Haroun Tazieff. A great popularizer for his field in the Jacques Cousteau tradition and a Frenchman himself, Tazieff called the evacuation "utterly unnecessary." Although bad weather prevented him from getting a glimpse of the mountain firsthand, he freely delivered himself of some caustic advice about official overzealousness. "It's not a magmatic eruption of red-hot melted rocks," he said of St. Helens, "just low temperature explosion. It's spectacular, particularly for people who are not used to it, but absolutely not dangerous." Tazieff left town predicting that the volcano would probably "die out in a matter of days or weeks or months. According to all I've seen from the many pictures and conversations, lava will not appear during this eruption."

Donal Mullineaux, who knew the mountain's eruptive potential better than any man, didn't dispute the point. "Tazieff is right," he would say. "Compared to what this volcano has done in the past, so far we have a very minor event." But the quarantine stayed. The Survey would wait and watch.

News organizations grew bolder. A National Geographic helicopter developed fuel line problems at an opportune moment "forcing" it to land in the restricted area. When that story got around, one thing led to another, and by the following week a freelance team from Seattle was filming beer commercials at the crater's edge.

Another freelancer, Ancil Nance, after spending several days in a pup tent socked in by clouds in pursuit of the ultimate volcano picture, decided to take a more direct route: climb it. He convinced two friends to go along, including Pete Reagan, an accomplished mountaineer and, incidentally, Nance's family doctor. Afterward, Reagan likened the experience to a strenuous form of Russian roulette. "I don't think I've ever been so chronically frightened in my life," he recalls. "As a mountain climber, you cherish the illusion that you stay alive because you take care of yourself. On St. Helens, the climbing problem was trivial. All of the danger was beyond our control."

Harry Truman, 83 year old proprietor of St. Helens Lodge, captured the public imagination with his 'hell-no, I-won't-go' talk and penchant for bourbon and coke.

Besides, historically, Reagan pointed out, it's not the people who visit volcanoes, but those who live next to them, who die in eruptions. Along these lines, 83-year-old Harry Truman, proprietor of Mount St. Helens Lodge on Spirit Lake became an instant media star as the very prototype of the hard-bitten old geezer who wouldn't listen to bureaucratic reason. Truman had lived on the mountain for 54 years; his response to an evacuation order from the local sheriff was to lock the door. In fact, Harry's only concession to the nearly constant earthquake barrage was to move his bed into the basement.

Like the decisive President who shared his name, Harry came up with an early action plan for coping with the volcano. "I've said all along they ought to dump a bomb down that crater," he said. "Tear the thing right out of there, hair and guts and feathers and all."

A colorful character, Truman entertained reporters with his 1883 player piano, menagerie of 16 cats, and steady consumption of Schenley's bourbon and coke. He provided a human note of drama to the story and he knew it. "If I hadn't a been here, you tell me what the press and TV would've gotten out of St. Helens," he would challenge, and indeed, an odd sort of symbiotic relationship grew up. National Geographic staged an exclusive "event" for its cameras—helicoptering Harry over to a Salem-area grade school to thank the kids for their letters and concern. As for worrying about the mountain's threat to his life, "Just look at the mountain," he'd say, gazing through a window of his lodge, "beautiful, isn't she? That mountain will never hurt me. When you live someplace for 50 years, you either know your country or you're stupid."

Harry Truman puzzled the politicians. His hold on the popular imagination made him untouchable. But if he could stay in the red zone, why couldn't anyone else? Washington Governor Dixy Lee Ray, who had ordered the area's closure, apparently contradicted herself by commending Truman in a letter for his "independence and straightforwardness. When everybody else involved in the Mount St. Helens eruption appeared to be overcome by all the excitement," she said, "you stuck to what you knew and what common experience and sense told you. We could use a lot more of that kind of thinking, particularly in politics."

Common sense would have told Harry to leave. Towards the end, the mountain was being rocked by violent, frequent earthquakes which made him, in his words, "seasick." Some reporters felt that Truman was trapped by his national reputation—made when the mountain was relatively stable. He would have left, they figured, if he could have done so quietly. Truman's friends disagree, though. "Harry Truman was Spirit Lake," one said after the cataclysm. "Seeing what happened to it would have broke his heart."

The memorabilia inside the Lodge was like a peek inside Harry's heart at all he held dear—the mountain, hunting and fishing, and his beloved wife of 37 years, Edie. Her death in 1975 changed Harry, friends said, caused him to withdraw into a deep grief at the loss. Oddly enough, the mountain's stirring—with its attendant legion of reporters—brought him out of his blue mood for a time. As the TV crews filmed it all, Harry fired up his 1883 player piano once again and dared the mountain to come get him.

Ron Cronin

17

STRATO/COMPOSITE VOLCANO

By late April, an odd thing was happening. The volcano really wasn't front page news anymore. It had reached a plateau as measured by earthquakes and a few minor ventings of steam. Meanwhile, scientists were charting with utter fascination the growth of a giant lobe on the mountain's north flank. Their measurements indicated that Goat Rocks on the northwest face was being pushed up and out – perhaps by the magma climbing inside its chamber. No one knew the cause for sure, but the symptom was clear: like some pantagruelean pregnancy, the north flank was bulging outward at a steady rate of 5 feet per day. This "deformation rate" became a key statistic to monitor. However, on May 12 an avalanche dropped an 800-foot wide slab of ice, snow and gravel down both sides of Sugar Bowl Glacier. The Survey chose the better part of valor and abandoned its observation post at the timberline parking lot.

Even as the scientists sense of foreboding grew, property owners in the Spirit Lake area were getting increasingly impatient with the roadblocks. A bulge was one thing, but the mountain hadn't erupted in weeks. If an avalanche was imminent, they wanted to at least take out the more valuable furniture from their summer cabins at the mountain's base. Dave Smith, owner of Spirit Lake Lodge, thought the area should be opened up for tourists. "This is when we're making our money," he told a reporter. "The way the weather is now, this would be a bonanza."

Eventually, the owners decided to organize a protest caravan. Eager to avoid a confrontation, though, the Governor's office relented. A sheriff's car would lead a convoy from the roadblock to Spirit Lake the next weekend.

Saturday morning, 35 owners plus a handful of reporters signed waivers releasing state and county agencies from any blame, and proceeded into the area. They fed pets, loaded their pickups with microwave ovens, stereos, foosball tables. The landscape they found chilled them. It was a ghost of the glowing green they remembered. The trees were covered in ash; cabin porches sagged under the weight; the grass was being smothered. Some felt a heaviness in the air that made them hurry in their tasks. But as they left, the tension slipped away. The mountain hadn't moved. In fact, so many owners showed interest in returning that a second caravan was scheduled. Sign-up would begin the next morning for entry into the hazard zone around Spirit Lake at noon, Sunday, May 18th.

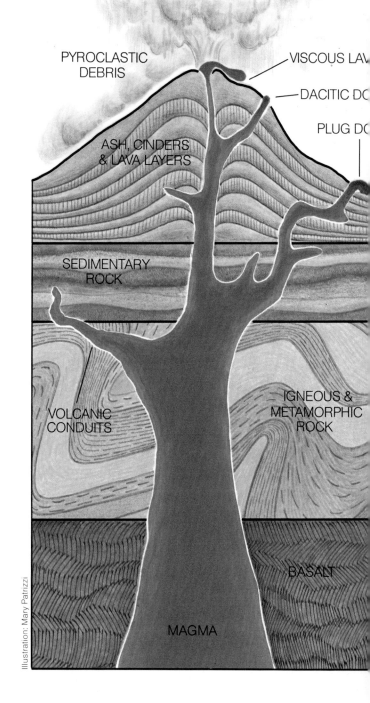

Ron Cronin

ere are many kinds of
lcanoes. Technically, geolo-
ts call Mount St. Helens a
ato-composite volcano. Non-
hnically, that means that
Helens is basically a large
ap of rubble left over from
evious eruptions—of ash,
desite lava, dacite domes,
mice and pyroclastic debris,
r the most part. When the
ountain began to stir in the
ring, geologists noted that its
rth face was bulging
tward. The probable cause
this distortion was the
agma body's rising up the
lcanic conduits and putting
mendous pressure on the
rth face to escape. By mid-
y, parts of the north slope
ted out over 400 feet from
eir previous angle of repose
e black dotted line is the
ountain's former silhouette)
using geologists to worry
out the possibility of a
astrophic avalanche into
irit Lake.

The red and white Cessna three-seater swung wide around
the mirror-smooth surface of Spirit Lake before making one
last pass over the crater. A young husband and wife team of
geologists, Dorothy and Keith Stoffel, had chartered the plane
out of Yakima for a Sunday morning view of the mountain.
Their pilot Bruce Judson had been cleared by Seattle traffic
control to enter the restricted airspace around the volcano
a few minutes before eight o'clock.

The day was flawless—blue skies, still air, a warming sun.
Theirs was the only plane in the area. The Stoffels didn't
know it yet, but today they would get a very special view
indeed—a close-up look at the decapitation of Mount St.
Helens. By a miracle of milliseconds, they survived to tell the
story, distilled here from Keith's report to the Washington
State Department of Natural Resources.

In their early circuits of the mountain, the Stoffels had
observed nothing unusual, no hint of the imminent apocalypse. By now the mountain's bloated appearance—its snowfields streaked with ash, its glaciers cross-hatched by giant
stress cracks big enough to swallow a house—had become
a familiar sight. Even the bulge, a continuing malignant
growth on the north face distending outward nearly 400 feet,
was barely noticeable against the mountain's vast scale.

The only motion evident was a tiny seep of steam issuing
from the south side of the crater. The scene struck the couple
as "tranquil"—too much so. On the last pass, they hoped the
mountain would do something photogenic. Send up a geyser
of steam. Maybe even a burst of ash. Something.

They weren't disappointed.

Its summit ruptured, Mount St. Helens hemorrhages a dense gusher of ash, hot rock and gas into the stratosphere on May 18, 1980.

As the Cessna approached the crater, 1000 feet over the west rim, Keith noticed a landslide starting on the inside of the crater wall. (Seismographs would record a pair of large quakes, over 5.0 on the Richter scale at 8:30 and 8:32 as the triggering mechanism for the eruption.) Pilot Judson dipped the wing for a better view. As he did so, before their disbelieving eyes, the entire northern half of the crater began to fibrillate, churning on itself more like a storm-tossed sea might do than a hunk of solid earth. Dust began to rise from the crater like so much spume. Everything on one side of an east-west sheer line was in rippling vertiginous motion while the other half remained solid, oblivious, stationary. This eerie palpitation persisted for about ten seconds until, abruptly, a mile-long crack opened across the crater floor, and, without more ado, says Keith Stoffel, "the north side of the mountain just slid away."

For a few seconds, the huge mass of the mountain – perhaps half a cubic mile of material in all, including the entire peak and the dacite lava plug which had so effectively bottled up the subterranean forces of the volcano – plunged downslope together like some great stricken ship. Then, gathering momentum, the striated layers of pumice, lava, tephra and ash laid down over the centuries shook loose, lost all form and avalanched in a dense roiling confusion. Millions of tons of pressure were suddenly removed from the mountain's innards. The magma that had been rising slowly up the volcano's vents for months now had almost no downward pressure on it at all.

The practically instantaneous result was a blast of incredible force. Geologists have estimated the magnitude of the explosion at 2500 times the power of the atom bomb that destroyed Hiroshima. Instead of bursting straight up, though, as is common in volcanic eruptions, the explosion followed the lateral line of least resistance – sideways to the north. The shock wave from the eruption, focused like a rifle shot by the intact semi-circle of the crater to the south, east and west, slammed across the miles of forest and up-country lakes to the north. A billion board feet of timber fell like so many pieces of straw.

For the Stoffels, watching the event unfold from only a few hundred feet above the maelstrom, the sequence had an eerie, dream-like quality. The deep-throated rumble of the blast would frighten people as far away as Canada. But right above it, the Stoffels heard nothing, felt nothing–not even any air turbulence.

Moments after the slope gave way, a jet of dense black smoke shot into the air, heavy with pulverized rock and ash that clung about the peak like a cement thunderhead. The low bristling cloud billowed out from its center in all directions, consuming the mountain from view and growing at a prodigious rate. "Can we outrun it?" Stoffel shouted at the pilot as the cauliflower heads of death bloomed in hot pursuit behind the tiny craft. Judson had already opened wide the throttle and put the Cessna into a dive to increase airspeed. "I don't know," he answered.

To be caught by the cloud was sure death. Hours later, a cropduster in eastern Washington would become the volcano's first confirmed victim when he crashed after being caught aloft in the surprise ash storm there.

Not until the three set down at Portland International Airport did they unclench the little fist of fear that held them in in their flight. Watching the eruption on TV, they were a conspicuously noisy presence in the airport's cocktail lounge. "I guess we were laughing too much," Judson recalls of the impatient looks people were giving them.

Laughing to be alive. They had peered down the very maw of a beast that would lick out to kill over 60 people that day, some of them 18 miles away–and lived to tell the tale.

In the seconds it took their plane to clear the eastern rim of the mountain, Harry Truman's lodge had already been flattened by the enormous shock wave. Before the cloud that menaced them had even begun welling up, several hundred feet of avalanche debris had buried Spirit Lake, sloshing its displaced waters up against the base of Mount Margaret and back into a wholly new, elevated basin–with an outlet to the North Toutle 200 feet higher than the old one. The lake itself had transmogrified into a steaming cauldron of mud, heated up with each new barrage of pyroclastic material that flowed into it from the lowered north lip of the crater. Three weeks after the cataclysm, at a spot between the newly formed lake and the crater, geologists would measure a temperature of 784 degrees Fahrenheit in material nine feet below the surface.

Close by the mountain, survival was almost exclusively a matter of where you were–either in the path of the blast or not. David Johnston was posted on the U.S. Geological Survey's campsite atop the Coldwater Creek drainage, one ridge removed from the base of the mountain and some five miles from the crater. His job was to run the equipment that was monitoring the rate of deformation on the worrisome bulge. Ironically, the Survey had moved back its observation post from timberline less than a week previously. Coldwater camp was considered a safe spot, should the north face give way.

(right) Bob Rogers was camped 11 miles to the West when the mountain exploded. Within minutes, the ash cloud enveloped him in a surrealistic contrail of volcanic grit, shutting out all light.

(below) More than 30 miles away, the city of Longview crouches under the apocalyptic vision of the ascending plume.

Kraig Scatterella

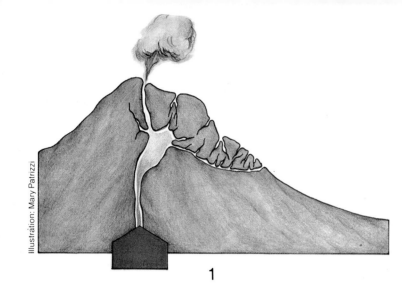

Illustration: Mary Patrizzi

1

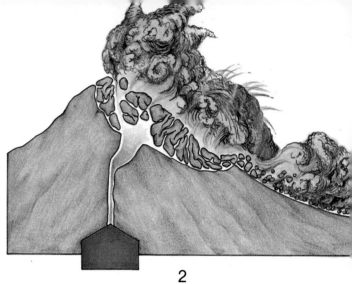

2

By the end of the day, the force of the eruption abates, revealing the reamed lip of the vastly enlarged crater.

Al Hayward

(below) On May 18, the seismographic record (as registered at Portland State University) shows a large earthquake at 8:30 a.m. under the mountain followed by another at 8:32 followed by an indistinguishable "swarm" of quakes–the eruption–for the next several hours.

M=5   M=5

Anatomy of a disaster (left): at 8:32, an earthquake of magnitude 5.0 or above shakes the mountain. The north face, already weakened by the magma pushing outward, gives way and begins to avalanche downward. Frame two: without the tremendous weight of the mountain to contain it, the sublimated gases inside the magma are free to expand, like a shaken champagne bottle with its cork removed. A lateral blast, focused to the north by the intact walls of the crater in all other directions, results. Frame three: the eruption goes to full throttle in a chain reaction. The more magma released, the less the pressure further down in the magma chamber and the greater the rush of gas to escape. Pyroclastic flows spill out the lowered north lip of the mountain and down towards Spirit Lake.

3

When it did, Johnston only had time to say into his radio, "Vancouver, Vancouver, this is it!" The blast's impact so thoroughly scoured the ridge that, days later, rescue crews couldn't even identify for certain the campsite. The hurricane winds given teeth by the pulverized rock and abrasive ash had swept away the Survey's 22-foot trailer, jeep, monitoring equipment, everything.

One ridge farther removed and slightly to the west, Reid Blackburn, a photographer for the Vancouver Columbian, was on assignment for the Survey and National Geographic magazine. He squeezed off several shots of the eruption–the ensuing heat would spoil the film–before retreating into the protection of his green Volvo. A rescue team found him there two days later, wrapped in a blanket and buried in ash, the car's windows punched out by the explosion.

Out of the direct line of the blast, the effects of the eruption became more haphazard, almost capricious, as the massive wave bounced off the sides of lesser mountains and broke into pockets of tornado-like turbulence. Woodburn area logger James Scymansky was part of a four-man crew

thinning trees on Weyerhaeuser Company land that morning. The ridge they were working–in the Green Mountain area just west of the blast zone, was only 7 miles from ground zero. Their chain saws drowned out the initial explosion but not the ash hissing through the trees that blotted out the sun. Moments later, a sudden wind knocked Scymansky down, carrying off his hard hat. "I thought we were dead," he recalls, "It was like the end of the world."

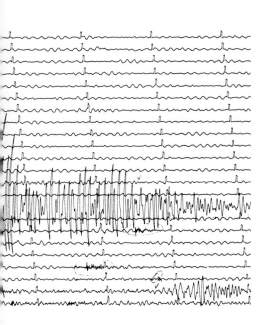

Ron Cronin

This sequence of photographs (right), taken over a 15 second span, shows the progress of a pyroclastic flow down the southwest face of the mountain during the height of the May 18 eruption. A pyroclastic flow consists of a superheated mixture of volcanic gases and ash and rock fragments. As it races downslope at speeds up to 200 mph, the ride is virtually frictionless because the mass "hydroplanes" on the cushion of gases given off by the incandescent pumice. The photographs clearly show great clouds of billowing white where the pyroclastic flow has flashed snow to steam on the instant of its passage.

Breathing itself became a painful compromise with survival. The air, thick with superheated particles of freshly expelled pumice and ash seared their lungs at each inhalation. Blinded by ash, the four stumbled down the logging road toward their pickup truck. Scorched trees, three feet in diameter, lay across the road, too large to jump, too hot to touch. The smashed truck offered no protection, so they continued walking down the road, mile after mile, under the incessant hail of fire. The pain from multiple burns became so great that, "I got to hoping something would wipe us out quickly," says Scymanski. Doctors would later treat him for burns over 53 percent of his body.

One of the other loggers, half-crazed by the inferno, wandered off towards the north fork of the Toutle, by now a steaming-hot cauldron of mud and uprooted trees. His body was recovered, suspended in a tree he climbed, several weeks later. For ten hours, the ordeal continued. The thought crossed Scymansky's mind that God was punishing him for working on Sunday.

At last, an air rescue helicopter spotted the three loggers and carried them to the Emanuel Hospital burn center. For all but Scymansky, though, help arrived too late; his companions died of complications arising from their injuries two weeks later.

An Air Force Reserve helicopter (below left) crew looks for survivors in the Tradedollar Lake area.

The morning after the eruption (below), vapors streamed from fumaroles across a confused landscape of other worldly shapes and smells.

Dave Wendt

The west arm of Spirit Lake (left) steamed with volcanic heat for a week after the blast.

On the west side of the mountain, courtesy of twentieth century technology, a national television audience shared a very nearly too-enterprising Seattle cameraman's brush with death by suffocation.

On a hunch, Dave Crockett had loaded up his gear in the middle of the night and headed for the mountain. Following his impulse, Crockett ended up only a few miles to the west of the volcano when it blew. As the turbulent, gray-black plume exploded overhead, he gunned his car away–back down a logging road. But a gush of glacial melt and mud beat him to the bottom of the ravine, knocking out the bridge which was his only exit.

The trapped Crockett grabbed his camera and started up a ridge. As the falling ash blacked out the light, he turned on his camera to film what he supposed were the last moments of his life. This footage, broadcast on national television, powerfully evokes the sheer terror felt by the volcano's victims. "Oh dear God, my God," Crockett trembles into his audio, "This is hell on earth. Right at this moment, I honest to God believe I am dead." The camera swings back and forth wildly as his footsteps scramble in the ash, its mechanical eye picking up an occasional silhouette in the claustrophobic darkness. Panting from fear and short of breath, the bitter taste of ash in his mouth, Crockett cries out his despair to the tape recorder: "It's a black hell, totally pitch-black. Dear God, help me breathe. I can't see a thing."

Fortunately for Crockett, the cloud of ash around the mountain resolved itself into a column fairly rapidly. A military helicopter picked him up, shaken but sound, that afternoon. By that time, the ash column reached 10 miles into the sky where the jet stream carried it off in the direction of eastern Washington and on across the nation.

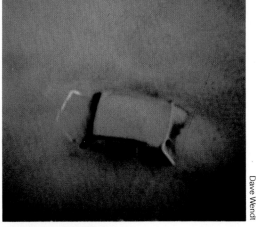

Vancouver Columbian *photographer Reid Blackburn's car (below) was nearly buried in ash. Blackburn was found inside, dead from suffocation.*

Dave Wendt

(opposite page) By mid-afternoon of the 18th, mudflows streak the mountain's flank and swell the Toutle River beyond flood stage, carrying everything in its path.

Dave Wendt

Four year old Bonnie Moore of Castle Rock was glad to see helicopter crews arrive on Monday morning to pick her family up from their demolished campsite near the Green River–and so was her three month old little sister, Terra Dawn.

Bruce Nelson and Sue Ruff (right) were camped next to Terry Crall and Karen Varner on the Green River. Nelson and Ruff survived the falling timber; Crall and Varner weren't so lucky.

Michael Lloyd

Michael Lloyd

Ancil Nance

In the blast's aftermath, trees lay in windrows, combed down in neatly regimented columns. Scientists are mapping the direction of tree fall in order to reconstruct the aerodynamics of the explosion.

In Yakima, they called the day Ash Sunday. The sky darkened at midday, as if an eclipse were in progress. But the darkness wouldn't lift. Street lights automatically turned on; neon lights glowed against the earthen blizzard. As the stuff began to accumulate, the artifacts of the good life – cars, air conditioners, sewage treatment plants – literally ground to a halt. In places like Moses Lake, Washington, motorists would be stranded for days before help could make it through. The Governor of Montana simply shut down the state for two days.

The ash looked like a fine sleet coming down. People instinctively reached for their coats and snow shovels. But it was hot out there, and the stuff wasn't melting.

In fact, the only melting taking place was back at the mountain, where the heat of the blast and successive pyroclastic flows was turning the frozen reservoirs of snowfields and glacial ice on the side of the mountain into a rampaging torrent. The Geological Survey has estimated that about 140,000 acre-feet of water – three times the volume of Spirit Lake – was thawed out within hours by the hot volcano. Mixed with half a cubic mile of avalanche material, uprooted trees, logging trucks, dead elk and just about anything else handy, this wall of yellow-brown muck pulsed down the mountain's drainages at levels up to 60 feet above flood stage.

300 families lost their homes along the Toutle in the ensuing flood; seven of eight bridges were washed out; 5000 acres of farmland were inundated, as was much of the town of Castle Rock. The Toutle itself was running half mud, half water, suffocating any life which hadn't already been boiled away by its 100 degree plus temperatures. Flows were so high that the Toutle backed up the Green River, forcing its channel through a nearby fish hatchery. 12 million salmon fingerlings were killed. So were three loggers, swept away along with the better part of a Weyerhaeuser logging camp.

Early the next morning, long-time Columbia river pilot John Satalich got the surprise of his life. While guiding the bulkloaded ship Hoegh Mascot into port, he grounded her out. "I was in utter disbelief," he says of the event. As well he might have been. The ship was square in the middle of the channel at the time.

Satalich thus became the first to discover the impossible. The Toutle, by way of the Cowlitz River, had nearly filled a ten mile stretch of the 600 foot wide by 40 foot deep Columbia channel overnight. In a little less than 24 hours after the eruption. The Toutle River had transported enough material from the flanks of St. Helens to the Columbia to fill a string of dump trucks 500 miles long – some 21 million yards of debris in all. A flotilla of dredges would require several months and $64 million dollars to partially undo the damage.

San Francisco Examiner reporter Ivan Sharp is hoisted to safety after he dodged roadblocks and his car stuck on an ash-clogged logging road. Prop wash stirred up the ash whenever helicopters neared the ground, so rescue crews quickly learned to rely on the use of the sling hoist.

(below) A paramedic provides oxygen to a man evacuated from the south fork of the Toutle River.

Dave Wendt

Kraig Scatterella

And that was only the tip of the economic fallout from the volcano. Farm crops across the West had been damaged, perhaps irretrievably. Tourism would be stifled. The Washington Department of Fish and Wildlife estimated that over a million and a half wild animals–including sizeable elk and deer herds, bear, cougar, bald eagle and mountain goats, as well as half a million game fish, had been killed.

The mountain itself was clothed in a concealing mantle of clouds, embarrassed with her smoldering, broken form, some journalists fancifully suggested. Not to be denied a look, though, the Air National Guard trained its Side-Looking-Advanced Radar (SLAR) on the peak to come up with an image that struck hurt into the hearts of the mountain's many admirers. Gone was the Fujiama of America. In its place appeared a vision of the eviscerated hulk, more crater than mountain. In high contrast black and white, the SLAR photo showed a portrait of Apocalypse Here, volcano-style. 1300 feet of the peak had been blasted off the south side; an astonishing 3000 feet on the north. In one fell swoop, St. Helens had gone from Washington's fifth highest peak to about its thirtieth. The volcano probably wasn't even high enough to build glaciers anymore.

Indians suggested a divine and vengeful providence was at work for disturbing their ancient burial grounds with the floodwaters of a new dam. Environmentalists made veiled references about the mountain finally getting even for the atrocious clear-cuts on its flanks. Jim Scymanski figured the eruption was punishment for working on Sunday. Surely, everyone in their innermost being knew the secret guilt which had excited this wrath.

And yet no one knew. For what moves a mountain, besides the slowly toiling continental plates and the laws of physics? When the mountain's motives were set aside, a single fact remained: the volcano had given; and now, the volcano had taken away.

Mudflows the consistency of liquid concrete effortlessly carried away any object in their path. Here, a four-wheel drive vehicle alongside the Toutle has been wrapped around a tree, battered beyond recognition.

Parajumpers (below) prepare to lift a body into a helicopter for transfer to a makeshift morgue at the Toledo airstrip.

Ron Cronin

Dave Wendt

The grim task of searching for what anyone would least want to find stretched on for weeks after the eruption. Near Elk Rock, a sleeping bag with a wallet tucked inside it was discovered–but not its owner. Ultimately, the remains of 30 of the mountain's 62 victims were located.

Tim Jewett

Those who entered the devastated area the day after the blast in search of survivors make an insistent claim. There was something about the yellow sulfurous light that day. Something about the way the low scudding clouds mixed with the steam from hundreds of fumaroles on the ground to confuse even the basic airman's instinct for heaven and earth, up and down. Those men who worked on the rescue missions aren't sure exactly what it was, but they are sure about this much: the day after the blast, the area around Mount St. Helens simply didn't look to be a part of this world.

By Wednesday, it did. The rains had come, and the rivulets, streams, newly-dammed lakes, meandering rivers of dark gray mud, had started to form a drainage network that defined the land in a somewhat familiar way. Immediately after the blast, though, the airmen could make out nothing: St. Helens had left a landscape at once disturbing to every sense of equilibrium about the natural world and pristine in its utter surrender to chaos.

Up to his brisket in mud, police dog Hauser (left) rests after searching a campsite by scent for human remains. The rain proved both bane and boon for the search parties. The mud it created was extremely difficult to move around in. However, the rain settled the ash and exposed victims who otherwise would not have been found.

Tim Jewett

Looking down the east lobe of Spirit Lake at what's left of the mountain's north face. The picture closely matches the vantage point of the Mount St. Helens profile on page six. However, because the catastrophic avalanche filled in the old lake basin, raising the water level by 150 feet, an exact duplication was impossible. Trees that once adorned the hillsides now choke the lake's surface.

© Gary Braasch

An army helicopter pilot on Monday radioed his command post that Spirit Lake had "disappeared." That's not a common event for a body of water that covers over 1200 surface acres, and he turned out to be wrong. But the story underlines how easy it was to become completely disoriented in this stricken, monochrome land, even from the air. On the ground, weeks later, fire crews brought in to put out hundreds of smoldering logs discovered that it behooved them to mark their path back to the helicopter with phosphorescent orange flags. Otherwise, they got lost in minutes. Geologists tending their experiments noticed that they attracted hummingbirds as they moved about in the empty quarter–their bright shirts were the only candidate flowers for miles around.

What little wildlife survived the eruption behaved in a stunned, erratic fashion. One rescue crew approached a doe that had stopped in the middle of an ash-smothered logging road. The animal didn't flinch: it lay down instead. They considered putting an end to her suffering by slitting her throat, but decided not to. The next morning the deer was back on its feet, gone.

It wasn't a place for the living, yet. Scientists measuring the temperature of pyroclastic flows found their boots burning from the residual heat. Judging by the melted mag wheels on an overturned pickup truck, the thousands of acres of flattened trees, the utter silence, broken only by the whomp-whomp-whomp of helicopter blades, nothing could have survived here. So the search crews moved into the fringe areas, places where the trees still stood, though dead, their needles turned red in the volcanic furnace. Maybe, just maybe, someone had stayed alive here.

More often, though, the rescuers came upon chilling tableaus of death, some with a Pompeiian touch of the timeless domestic moment: there was the retired couple found transfixed in their camper, he with a camera in his hands as if to take one last snapshot; the young lovers in their tent, encircled in each others arms to the end.

There was also the odd and unaccountable. A rescue team investigating a late-model white station wagon along old highway 504 above Camp Baker on the North Fork of the Toutle found two bodies–that of a man just outside the car and a woman inside. Beside her on the front seat was a satchel full of "white material" and a roll of $100 dollar bills. A wholesale shipment of cocaine.

Major Dave Wendt, a helicopter pilot with the U.S. Air Force Reserve's 304th Rescue Unit out of Portland, was flying a stretch of ruined countryside beside the Green River near Fawn Lake, the morning after. To his surprise, he spotted first a red speck in the expanse of gray, then, a couple with a child waving from atop a downed, denuded tree. "I couldn't believe it," recalls Wendt. "The area they were in looked like a bombing range."

The dust was too heavy to allow a landing, so Wendt moved his ship back a couple of thousand yards and hoisted down a couple of "p.j.'s"–para-jumpers–to guide the family to a suitable pick-up spot. When Sergeant Dick Harter reached them,, he reported surprising news back to the pilot; "We've got four healthy survivors here and one of

Would-be adventurer Otto Sieber and his campfollowers were helped out of their own miscalculation after a trek into the devastated zone turned into a self-described "death march."

Dave Wendt

them would like to have a word with you." Over the radio came the sound of a baby crying. It was three month old Terra Dawn Moore of Castle Rock, Washington, protesting with all her might the catastrophic eruption of a volcano during her first backpacking trip ever. "That moment made the whole rescue effort worthwhile for me," says Wendt.

Later, Mike and Lu Moore described how they had sought refuge from the hot ash, together with their children in an elk hunters lean-to. Mike found a spring for drinking water and they had their sleeping bags for warmth. Terra Dawn was still being breast fed so food wasn't a pressing problem. The only thing that really had her afraid, Lu admitted later, was that she might get airsick in the helicopter.

37

All told, helicopter crews airlifted nearly 200 people out of volcanic harm's way, mainly homeowners and fishermen from alongside the rampaging Toutle. The Moores proved to be the last survivors to be found in the devastated area. After Monday, the rescue mission tacitly turned to the grim task of recovering bodies. The long nose of a police dog named Hauser gained a modicum of fame for his uncanny ability to sniff out decaying human flesh from under the ash blanket. As for the rescue teams wielding the shovels, they smoked cheap cigars. Eventually, about half of the mountain's 62 victims would be recovered. A coroner's report confirmed that most had suffocated, their lungs clogged with ash.

About four days after the eruption, helicopter crews began to notice that they were now "rescuing" people who illegally had entered the devastated zone after the blast. Particularly galling to the airmen was the case of one Otto Sieber.

In Mid-April, Sieber led a team of cameramen up the grumbling volcano in defiance of the Forest Service quarantine. Backed up by a helicopter in case of difficulty and wearing camouflaged white with ashen gray clothes, their ascent went off without a hitch. The Sieber team even staged a picnic on the mountain's summit and filmed two versions of a beer commercial there in order "to recoup some of the expenses."

Sieber next went to the <u>Seattle Times</u> with the story of his adventure, gathering a fair amount of pubicity in the process. He solemnly warned others against following his example, though: "I personally would not go back for $100,000" he said. Too dangerous.

Nonetheless, after the eruption, he and an even larger camera crew returned–this time to make a film documentary about the devastation. However, slogging around in the mud proved surprisingly difficult. The weather turned foul–wet and cold. The mountain erupted, showering the team in ash. After only three days, the gay lads found themselves in a struggle to stay alive. By the time a helicopter came to their rescue, near Tradedollar Lake, several of Sieber's crew were suffering from hypothermia and Sieber himself, half-blinded by ash, had to be led to the helicopter.

It wasn't the first case of trespass, nor was it the last. Something about the volcano seemed to lead men on, moth-like, toward the flame of danger that burns at the very center. And lest we gloat too long over Sieber's comeuppance, best to remember there's a little bit of volcano voyeur in each of us.

The tourist shop hastily set up alongside the spot where the highway up the Toutle River valley transforms into a mile-wide mudflow has a guest book inscribed with the signatures of curiosity-seekers from around the world–from Australia, New Zealand, Japan, Brazil. We may have boycotted their Olympics, but the Russians have visited our volcano. Even President Carter, described in one local newspaper as "the biggest gawker of them all," made the tour. It rained that day, but he inspected the devastated area anyway, commenting: "It makes the surface of the moon look like a golf course." Another Carter observation, though teased at by the press, may prove prophetic: "One day, this will be as big a tourist attraction as the Grand Canyon," he said.

For the time being, however, most of the tourists are of the scientific stripe. The difference between scientist and garden variety rubbernecker is not as profound as you might suppose. Inside the devastated zone, the scientists do their share of ooh-ing and ah-ing. Like us common folk, they're curious. It's just that scientists are systematic about their curiosity–and have devised truly astounding instruments to extend their powers of observation.

For instance, on the morning of the big blow, a heat-sensitive picture of the north side taken at 6:30 in the morning showed several new hot spots around the Goat Rocks area–where the mountain was to give way two hours later.

When St. Helens did explode, satellite pictures from outer space recorded the force of the blast bouncing off the cloud cover several hundred miles away. A weather radar trained on the plume in mid-eruption looked through the ash to detect solid chunks of material the size of five pickup trucks being hurled 49,000 feet in the air.

Geophysicists on St. Helens have kept track of alterations in the mountain's shape with laser beams and tiltmeters–instruments so sensitive they could detect the change in slope of a half-mile long board if you were to raise one end by the thickness of a dime. They have used seismographs to monitor the mountain's every rumble; remote-control cameras, barographs and thermometers for probing into mud and pyroclastic flows; U-2 planes and mass spectrometers for analyzing the make-up of the gases in the plume. Each of these tools has added to the basic fund of raw data about the volcanic process in the Cascades.

In fact, it would scarcely be an exaggeration to call the eruption at Mount St. Helens the best documented in the history of mankind. No doubt, an abundance of new theories will flow out of the effort to assimilate this data. In the end, though, scientists, freelance adventurers and householders atop their roofs watching the latest plume billow heavenward were caught up by the same fascination. If the processes of a volcano are the processes of creation, then St. Helens presented that sweetest of all spectacles: creation watching itself become.

*President Carter
prepares to survey the havoc
wreaked by the May 18
eruption. Foul weather
obscured the peak, but Carter
was able to "see" it anyway,
thanks to a radar image of
the blown-out crater taken just
hours before.*

Overleaf: A panoramic camera presents a spectacular comparison of the mountain's northern sector before and after the May 18 catastrophic eruption. The initial portrait was made the morning of April 12 at an altitude of 5000 feet from atop the hills overlooking the main lobe of Spirit Lake. The second shot was taken from the same location the morning of August 10.

A panoramic camera takes in a full 180 degrees of the horizon. It does so with minimal distortion by swiveling on its tripod in one direction while a single continuous strip of film inside the camera rotates simultaneously in the opposite direction. In this case, the photographer has captured all the landmarks on the horizon from Mount Adams, past due east of St. Helens, to the peaks area of Mount Margaret to the west. To get the full sense of sweep from the photographs, arrange the gatefold in a semicircle and turn your head as you look.

The mudflow put a new floor under this child's swing. With ropes shortened a few feet, it'll be as good as new. Whether the tree's roots will be able to breathe through the dense layer of mud is another question.

This 1920s vintage Fordson tractor (opposite page) will need more than its famed pulling power to free itself from the clammy embrace of a Cowlitz River valley mudflow. 5000 acres of agricultural land were inundated by mud.

Ron Cronin

Randy Wood

When the mud flows came through their homes, people made hasty choices, saved what they could.

42

Ron Cronin

43

An eastern Washington farmer (left) examines damage to his asparagus crop. In general, row crops came through the ash barrage fairly well while wheat, barley and alfalfa suffered. State agriculture officials put the loss at about 10 percent of Washington's annual crop and livestock production.

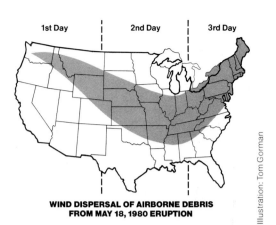

**WIND DISPERSAL OF AIRBORNE DEBRIS
FROM MAY 18, 1980 ERUPTION**

1st Day   2nd Day   3rd Day

A Wapato, Washington farmer drives through his vineyard. Agricultural experts said the ash chemically amounted to a low-grade fertilizer. One Yakima cannery took to bottling the ash and selling it, not as a gimmick, but to call attention to the benefits from the ash's trace elements. "If it weren't for ancient eruptions of this nature," a Sno-Kist spokesman explained, "we wouldn't have the outstanding quality of soil and fruit we have."

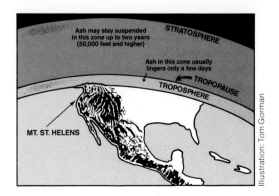

Ash may stay suspended in this zone up to two years (50,000 feet and higher)

STRATOSPHERE

Ash in this zone usually lingers only a few days

TROPOPAUSE

TROPOSPHERE

MT. ST. HELENS

Yakima was hard hit by the ashfall. Above, storeowners in this farm community 85 miles east of the volcano worked feverishly to move the heavy ash off flat roofs before they collapsed. An enterprising radio station weighed the amount of ash on one square foot of undisturbed roof, and came to the conclusion that 800,000 tons of the stuff had fallen within the city limits.

Everyone could see Friday the 13th approaching on the June calendar. The moon would be full, the mountain was poised, quiet. Reporters asked: did the Geological Survey expect another eruption? "It'll set science back 10 years if the mountain goes off on Friday," joshed spokesman Pete Rowley early in the week.

It did. Magnificently indifferent to its impact on science–or anything else–St. Helens let loose again just three hours ahead of the triskaidekaphobic witching hour with a moonlit plume that pulsed up to 50,000 feet and continued through the night. Caught by a perverse, meandering wind, the ash landed to the west, in the relatively densely populated Willamette Valley. For Portlanders, Friday dawned an unlucky morning indeed.

For one thing, there was the ad campaign kicking off that day in national newspapers, paid for by the Greater Portland Convention and Visitors Association. Its headline read: "The only Portland Ash left is in California Gift Shops." The city had gotten a light dusting two weeks ago, and wanted to dispel the notion that it wasn't a good place for tourists to visit. Portland, the ad continued "is still the clean green 'most livable' city in the U.S. it's always been."

As a matter of fact, though, the surprise Friday the 13th ashfall had dumped several tons of ash in Portland per city resident. True, there was only a sixteenth of an inch of the stuff on the ground. Alternatively, were that ash to arrive in boxcars, a television commentator noted, it would have required a train nearly 200 miles long to deliver it. The ads were pulled.

The ash presented a number of novel problems. For the first time in history, sponsors of the Rose Festival Grand Floral Parade, scheduled to go on the next day, found themselves praying for rain–to keep the dust down. As the Festival's director counted up the red ink, his thoughts turned to next year; "I wish we could put a concrete cap on that mountain," he said.

Indeed, the mountain has made life inconvenient in a number of unexpected ways. Abrasive ash makes everything from the brake pads on cars to the white lines on streets wear out quicker. It spoils crops and may increase soil erosion. It conducts electricity when wet and baffles bank cash machines. Part of it is magnetic and clings to iron. It settles on the table a half hour after dusting. For goodness sakes, it might even make jogging unhealthy.

Early on, physicians raised the question of whether chronic low-level exposure to the ash might not cause silicosis–a respiratory disease ordinarily associated only with industrial settings. The answer was: no one knew for sure, but probably not. Washington and Idaho got into a shouting match over whether breathing the stuff was dangerous. Washington said maybe; Idaho said no. "It doesn't seem to matter," one Idaho official slyly noted. "You seem to keep right on breathing it anyway."

Ron Cronin

Humor might disguise it, but in an irritating way the volcano had struck at the very soul of the Northwest's nascent identity – as the country blessed by nature. So what was so splendid about living next to this industrial accident masquerading as a mountain? What was so livable about a million people wandering the streets with big smiles drawn onto their face masks? With the second or third dousing of ash, citizens quietly absorbed a geologic verity: an active volcano may remain active for a long time. In the 1800s, St. Helens sounded off now and again over a 25 year period. The situation was beyond the control of concrete caps, H-bomb emetics, or clever ad campaigns.

Volcano or no, the Northwest remains a beautiful place, uncommonly close to nature – but nature on its own terms, the mountain has reminded us, not on ours.

Portland only received a light dusting, but in a big city environment, that was more than enough to take the bloom off the 1980 Rose Festival, the city's traditional spring frolic.

Magnified a thousand times under a scanning electron microscope, a grain of ash (below) shows up as a prickly customer indeed. The abrasive ash pitted a commercial jetliner's wings and windshield on May 18, causing it to make an emergency landing. People in the ash zone worried about its long-term effects on their health.

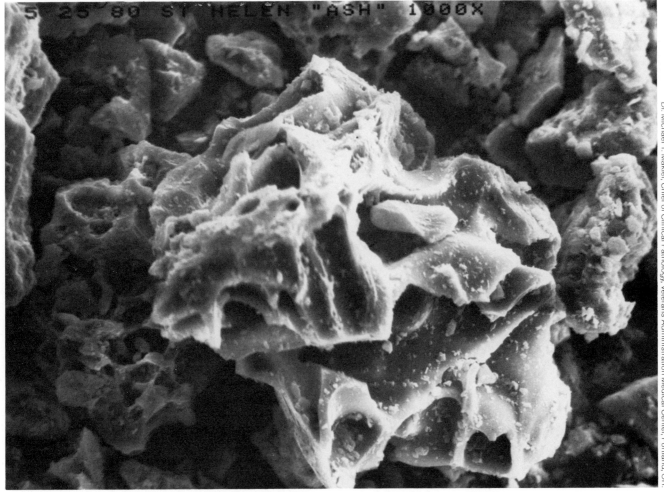

Dr. Michael T. Makler, Chief of Clinical Pathology, Veterans Administration Medical Center, Portland, OR.

National Aeronautics and Space Administration U-2 color infrared photography of the St. Helens area. The photograph on this page was taken on May 2, the one opposite was taken on June 19– after the big eruption. Red indicates anything green and growing. In the "before" picture, the outlines of the national forest are clearly visible, reflecting the fact that the private timber holders had clearcut right up to its boundaries. After the blast, Spirit Lake's old shape is indicated by a yellow line superimposed on the new lake's surface. The lake was considerably enlarged by the eruption.

NASA U-2/courtesy U.S. Forest Service

48

The moon's mysterious pull on the volcano symbolizes man's incomplete understanding of the eruptive process. Did St. Helens explode in phase with the moon's tidal pull? Were wild animals aware of the impending catastrophe days before it occurred? Will the May 18 eruption cause the world's climate to cool? In the wake of the blast, scientists are pursuing these and other far-reaching questions.

Illustration: Tom Gorman

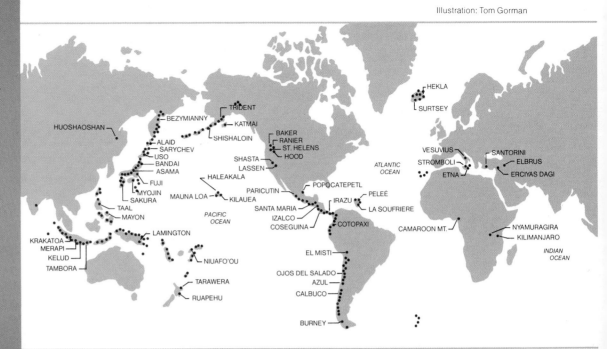

HEKLA
SURTSEY

BEZYMIANNY
TRIDENT
KATMAI
SHISHALOIN

HUOSHAOSHAN
ALAID
SARYCHEV
USO
BANDAI
ASAMA
FUJI
MYOJIN
SAKURA
TAAL
MAYON

BAKER
RANIER
ST. HELENS
HOOD
SHASTA
LASSEN
HALEAKALA
PARICUTIN
MAUNA LOA
KILAUEA

VESUVIUS
STROMBOLI
ETNA

SANTORINI
ELBRUS
ERCIYAS DAGI

ATLANTIC
OCEAN

POPOCATEPETL
PELEÉ
IRAZU
LA SOUFRIERE
SANTA MARIA
IZALCO
COSEGUINA
COTOPAXI

PACIFIC
OCEAN

LAMINGTON

KRAKATOA
MERAPI
KELUD
TAMBORA

NIUAFO'OU

CAMAROON MT.

NYAMURAGIRA
KILIMANJARO

INDIAN
OCEAN

TARAWERA
RUAPEHU

EL MISTI

OJOS DEL SALADO
AZUL
CALBUCO

BURNEY

There are over 600 active volcanoes in the world, 200 of which are shown on this chart. Most of them occur around the Pacific "Ring of Fire"–an imaginary line that circumscribes the Pacific Ocean and runs from southern Chile on up through the Pacific Northwest and Aleutian Chain across to Kamchatka in the Soviet Union, Japan, Indonesia and out into the Pacific. This wavy line corresponds precisely to where the spreading oceanic plate dives under the much larger plates upon which the continents rest. In the "Ring of Fire," Oregon and Washington are unusual insofar as they have active volcanoes but aren't bothered by the strong earthquakes usually associated with vulcanism.

Ancil Nance

Worldwide, an eruption the size of Mount St. Helens occurs infrequently, perhaps once in ten years. The explosion itself is nothing if not spectacular; the aftermath, however, affects ecosystems far removed in ways we are only beginning to understand. Among other things, the volcano has been blamed for the cold, wet summer of 1980 in England and France–not by a crackpot, but by an expert in climate research, Professor Hubert Lamb.

A professor of air chemistry has demonstrated that a family of chemicals–the methyl halogens–hitched a ride on the ash when it was injected into the stratosphere on May 18. Once in the upper atmosphere, these chemicals attack the ozone layer, which shields us from the harmful ultraviolet rays emitted by the sun.

(below left)
A pyroclastic flow from the July 22 eruption overlays an earlier deposit from the May 18 event. The tephra in the later eruption is much coarser but "flows" in the same watery way–in the case shown below, some three miles from the crater.

This giant blister, a fleur du mal more than 400 feet across, was raised by the cooling process of hot pyroclastic material above the place where Harry Truman's Lodge once stood.

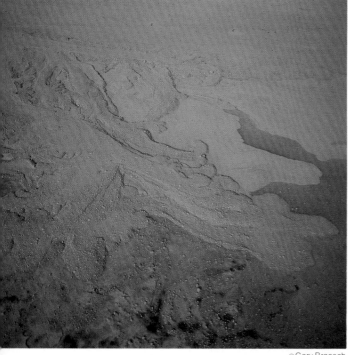

©Gary Braasch

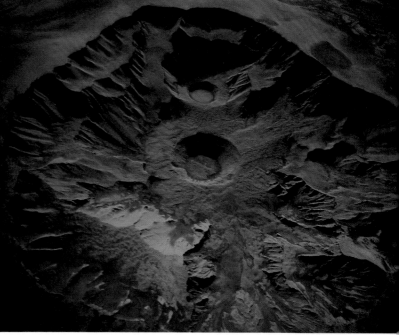

©Gary Braasch

For several days after the eruption, the Columbia River was carrying more sediment than the Mississippi does at flood stage. Bottom dwelling fish such as the starry flounder, English sole and Pacific tomcod were forced up to the surface. Sea lions abandoned the area. The bigger question, though, is what will happen to the benthic infauna–the bottom-dwelling worms–at the very foundation of the food pyramid in the estuary?

People in the multi-state area where the ash fell after the eruption will remember 1980 as the summer of no mosquitos. Entomologists report that the ashfall has acted as a giant application of insecticide across millions of acres of land. Here's how: under a microscope, particles of silica-rich ash show up as tiny shards of abrasive glass, bristling with dozens of dagger-like cutting edges. The ash has the effect of cutting the waxy covering of insects that retains their body moisture. When it's pierced, the insects dehydrate and die.

Unfortunately, that's bad news for the rest of the ecosystem. Many fish feed almost exclusively on protein-rich insect hatches–ask any fly fisherman. So do the young of rangeland game birds like the sage grouse and chukar partridge. Farmers aren't known for their love of insects in general, but they do hate to see a field of seed alfalfa go unpollinated for lack of bees.

As these examples imply, in the aftermath of the big boom, Mount St. Helens has become a laboratory for scientific inquiry. Some of these investigations have a very practical cast. Weapons strategists are analyzing the time and heaviness of downwind ash deposit across the United States for possible lessons on how radiation fallout from a nuclear bomb might behave. Gulf Oil is comparing the dynamics of the St. Helens horizontal blast with Tertiary (70 million years ago) volcanic sites it owns in Nevada that are now producing oil and gas.

Fumarole craters formed by explosions of hot steam rock the south shore of Spirit Lake. For several days after the eruption, these fumaroles would regularly send up geysers of steam two and three thousand feet in the air. Now, as the lake's water table rises, the craters are filling, too. Algae blooms in their warm water (left), one of the first visible signs of life reclaiming the blast zone.

Most of the geologic field work, though, is the data gathering backbone of the discipline – where did the tephra fall, what was its chemical makeup, and so on. The Geological Survey, which is anxious to improve its ability to foretell eruptions, may have made a breakthrough in this regard. In the case of St. Helens, the invisible gas plume constantly billowing out of the crater seems to give the best clue. Survey scientists have noted that, a matter of days before eruptions, the ratio of sulfur dioxide to carbon dioxide in the plume abruptly shifts. For the peace of mind of those working in the area, this kind of predictive tool is invaluable.

While occasionally it seemed that the paraphernalia of technology – correlation spectrometers, microbarographs and tiltmeters – had wholly appropriated the volcano, aspects of the event defied instrumentation. For instance, A Salem housewife named Charlotte King puzzled scientists by her ability to "hear" earthquakes on the mountain moments before their seismometers did. A property owner told biologists of an unusual number of elk migrating away from the mountain through his area days prior to the blast. Was it a valid observation? If so, to what signal could the human mind be tuned to better decipher the volcano's warning?

Lakes of all colors appear in the devastated area. This one (left), a milky green, is a remnant of the great mudflow down the Toutle Valley. Eventually, the reforming Toutle River must work its way through the mud lahar, filling depression after depression on its stairstep journey to join the still flowing section just above Camp Baker.

Two and one half months after the May 18 eruption, Spirit Lake (below left) is regaining its deep blue reflection. It now mirrors the scraped-clean basin around it, the trees blown down by the blast and swept away by the water's explosive rise and slosh as millions of tons of avalanche material thundered into it.

The striking brick red color of this chain of new lakes (above) in the Toutle drainage may come from dissolved minerals or from algae.

A stringer canyon (left) has been effectively dammed by the Toutle River mudflows, forming yet another lake. In the course of a few winters, the rains will erode through the levee.

A typical subalpine forest community (above left). After six inches of tephra has covered the area (above right), the forest takes on a ghostly aura. Most of the shrubs have been buried and the tree limbs bend under the weight of the ash.

Sediment-laden water forms a delta in a new lake (left), which, in turn, is looking for an exit further down the Toutle valley. Sedges, bog orchids and other swamp plants will take advantage of the many shallow lakes created by the mudflow.

The big eruption coincided with the tail end of the spring run of Chinook salmon up the Cowlitz River. In a survival test, biologists determined that adult chinook could only last in the river six hours before the sharp-edged ash cut their gills to shreds. Ordinarily, of course, salmon returning from the ocean seek out the stream where they were spawned with monomaniac inflexibility. All of this led hatchery officials to write off the rest of the Chinook run as a dead loss.

A couple of days later, though, tagged-Cowlitz salmon began to turn up en masse at the Kalama River hatchery – the next river upstream on the Columbia's north side. Faced by the hostile conditions on the Cowlitz, the Chinook adapted in a way biologists didn't believe possible. "They're smarter than we thought," admitted a surprised but pleased fishery expert.

In fact, biologists have a great deal to learn about the resiliency of natural systems. The 150 square miles of forested area destroyed by the volcano may be a logger's nightmare, but it's a naturalist's dream. The blast zone represents an incredible opportunity to students of natural succession – to watch a climax ecosystem build itself up from scratch.

June Lake on the southeast side of the mountain, was created centuries ago by mudflows similar to the May 18, 1980 one which has enlarged it, inundating young fir and hemlock on its western shore.

The process of recovery will differ according to the damage done. The hillsides above Spirit Lake had their face ripped off–right down to bedrock. There, nature must start from the very beginning by building back the soil in a process that could take centuries. Further out, the trees were leveled and ash or mudflow covers the land. In this zone, within weeks, the shaping hand of a natural order impatient with the void could be seen at work.

A frozen wave of mud two feet thick encircles a fir tree in the Swift Creek area. Needle fall begins the slow process of reforming the forest duff.

Portland State University geophysicist Ansel Johnson (above) places a tiltmeter on the southeast side of the mountain near June Lake. Results will be used to interpret settling of Mount St. Helens in the aftermath of the eruption.

Up through the ash they arose–ferns, mountain lupine, salmonberry, skunk cabbage, horsetail. Jerry Franklin, a plant ecologist with the Forest Service, discovered that young trees–especially Pacific silver fir–that had been buried in snow banks weathered the superheated air from the blast inside their insulated blankets quite well, thank you. These trees, when they grow up, may pioneer the reseeding of the empty quarter.

Another important transition tree is likely to be red alder. Ordinarily, foresters consider alder an undesirable blemish in the evergreen stands of the Northwest, and spray with herbicides to get rid of it. However, alder may hold the key to soil enrichment. It is a nitrogen fixer–capable of pulling this vital element out of the air and implanting it in the ash and pumice, where a succeeding generation of evergreens will thrive on it. Alder also has a winged seed, enabling it to propagate itself over appreciable distances.

A few weeks after the eruption, a Soil Conservation Service team found grass growing on top of a layer of ash, which itself sat on top of a couple of feet of snow. Obviously, this discovery meant that seed blown into the empty quarter had already germinated and begun to grow following the cataclysm. This finding is consistent with the Katmai volcanic eruption experience in Alaska at the turn of the century. Only four years after that blast, visitors to the "Valley of a Thousand Smokes" found large areas covered by lush stands of native grasses.

Although most insects were killed by the ash, ant colonies appear to be relatively resistant to its abrasive qualities. Ant hills have begun popping up through mud flows and ash falls; naturalists speculate that these insects will play an important role in the aeration of the mud and ash.

These incipient signs of recovery shouldn't surprise us too much. One look at a cross-section of the layered bands of volcanic debris that make up the St. Helens surround establishes an obvious fact: there's nothing new in this episode. The climax ecosystem has remade itself before. The once and future Spirit Lake was formed by pyroclastic debris and mudflows across the Toutle River. This time, however, there may be a significant difference.

Man the changer is on the scene. Not content to wait generations, man is eager to put the destroyed territory back to work, partly for economic reasons, partly to heal a psychic wound–the one inflicted on May 18 by the example of the volcano's uncontrollable might. For instance, by mid-July steelhead had already been spotted in the waters of the Toutle nosing their way back upstream. However, the Army Corps of Engineers is well aware that the Toutle and Cowlitz's flow carrying ability has been reduced by 90 percent by the mudflows filling up the old river beds. Hence, to avoid massive flooding in the Castle Rock and Longview communities in the rainy season, the Corps has undertaken the construction of huge, emergency debris dams. Unfortunately, the dams make no provision for the upstream passage of the colonizing steelhead.

Well-sorted cobbles from a centuries-old mudflow (directly below) were exposed and washed clean by flooding on Swift Creek. The result is a rockwall that would be the envy of an accomplished stone mason.

13 layers of ash and mudflow laid down over the centuries are evident in this cross-section (below) of Mount St. Helens soil. An eruption may be new to most of us, but it isn't to the mountain's ecosystems.

Even simple choices can get complicated. The timber industry wants to go into the devastated zone to remove downed timber as soon as possible. Logs lose their economic value after a couple of years out in the weather. On the other hand, left to nature's devices, those logs would rot and become the soil for the next generation of vegetation. As they decomposed, the windrows of fallen timber, placed across the hillsides, would form a kind of natural erosion barrier. Once the disintegration process was well advanced, helped along by insects, fungi, bacteria and mosses, seedlings would take root in the rich humous of the nurse-logs. Taking out the fallen timber has its cost: In the natural order, nothing is wasted.

One suggestion for the St. Helens area is the establishment of a national monument – a kind of volcano wilderness area – to leave at least the immediate blast area untouched by man so that the healing process may take place as it always has. The Forest Service expects to put forward its alternatives for the stewardship of the area within a few months. Whatever man decides, nature will remain perfectly relentless. No matter how many times the volcano erupts – and through the millenia there will be many indeed – the green forest will never tire of recreating itself.

The surprising power of water turgor (above) enables these young lupine to lift a six-inch crusted block of ash weighing more than a pound in their reach to light. Other successful plants in coping with heavy tephra deposits are beargrass, pearly everlasting, bracken fern and willow.
Biological damage on the west side of the mountain was markedly less than on the north.

(opposite page) Rain and ash form a cement-like casing around the upturned needles of Noble fir. The altitude-delayed summer shoots represent this tree's chance at survival.

Near Norway Pass, elk survey their former range (right), devoid of cover, forage or hope. Some of these survivors will migrate out of the area, but presumably, the surrounding forest was already at its carrying capacity. Biologists think most of these large animals, at the top of the herbivorous food chain, are fated to die in the winter.

Ron Cronin

George Colburn

©Gary Braasch

A carved beaver head, product of a New Deal craftsman's hand, looks over Mt. Hood's Timberline Lodge. When Hood shook several weeks after St. Helens erupted, an excitable populous wondered if this national historical monument would be the next volcano target.

For Dick Kohnstamm, the summer of 1980's celebration of his 25th anniversary on Mount Hood as manager of Timberline Lodge, the massive wood and stone showpiece of FDR's public works era, was marred by some bad news. In the wake of St. Helens' spectacular show across the river, sensors had detected a swarm of earthquakes under Hood. With a cosmic repertorial sense of deja vu, newspapers from Paris to San Francisco began chirping the imminent demise of his own particular peak.

In vain did Kohnstamm assure reporters that over the years he had experienced many tremors of similar size (this one toppled a can of beans off the shelf of a local supermarket.) After all, stratovolcanoes do weight a lot, consequently put stress on the earth's crust, and can occasionally be expected to shift a bit, like an old house settling.

After 50 quakes were recorded on the mountain within a week, though, the U.S. Geological Survey issued an official "hazard watch" and began its ritual setting up of a ring of seismometers around the mountain. Nine conventions booked into the Lodge canceled out. Hood River officials met at an emergency Saturday session to draft a volcano disaster evacuation plan. Headlines screamed from west to east.

Then, an embarrassing find. Seems that the competing ski resort on the other side of the mountain had been blasting out tree stumps when the earthquake "swarm" hit. A test was made. Sure enough, the fingerprint of the dynamite blasts matched "exactly" the seismic record of many of the so-called earthquakes.

End of mystery. Mt. Hood wasn't about to blow its top after all. Dick Kohnstamm expressed his deep disappointment in newspapers, TV reporters, the Geological Survey and everyone else involved in the public relations fiasco.

On the other hand, give Mt. Hood enough time, geologists guarantee, and it will surely erupt again, as inevitably as the continents are colliding. And so will they all—Lassen, Baker, Rainier, Shasta, up and down the coast. Perhaps millenia hence, perhaps this century. Contrary to the relatively smug view of only a few decades ago, the geological evidence suggests that the Cascade range is as volatile today as it has ever been. Up until St. Helens exploded, it was convenient to forget this fact. In California, for instance, the towns of McCloud, Weed and Mount Shasta have grown up atop the rubble of what is probably the most frightening of all volcanic phenomena—glowing avalanches. In western Washington, Mt. Rainier's historic mudflow valleys have been populated by several good-sized cities. For any one generation, the odds against catastrophe may be good. But as our civilization crowds its way onto the flanks of the Cascades, an inevitable result looms. Somewhere. Sometime.

Our reaction as a society to this new uncertainty is revealing. Less than a month after the eruption, a major corporation, National Semiconductor, announced that it was shelving plans to put a multimillion dollar plant into the Vancouver area because of the eruptions of Mount St. Helens. National Semi's headquarters are in Santa Clara, California, leading Vancouver city fathers to privately wonder among themselves what the company's top execs thought about the San Andreas fault? Obviously, though, a new uncertainty is different than an old one.

And don't forget the element of superstition. The Saint Helens School District had a tough time selling its bonds after the eruption. The interesting thing is the city of St. Helens isn't even in the same state as the volcano. It's in Oregon, but that didn't make investors any more comfortable with the name.

Locally, there's no doubt: it's psychically disorienting to have a familiar piece of the horizon vanish. Builders had been training living room windows on charming St. Helens for years. The new view is of a smoking black ruin. Some people resent this change, as though the mountain were a creature of animate judgment and will. Few, however, have taken their animosity to the extreme of self-described Spokane mountain man, Mark Perry.

Of all the odd St. Helens stories, his may be the oddest. The day before the lateral blast, he was climbing the peak, supposedly to take a picture of the crater. Luckily for him, on the way up he fell, dropped his movie camera (ruining it) and consequently had left the mountain's slopes by the time the cataclysm struck.

Far from frightened, Perry figured he had a score to settle with the mountain. So, he and a partner returned, wandering through the destroyed area for over a week snapping pictures of the forest ruins—until his friend turned an ankle and the pair had to be helicoptered out of the area. On top of this ignominy, Perry got more bad news. All the pictures he took were badly exposed and unusable.

So, a week later, Perry returned yet again—chip on shoulder still firmly in place. On this occasion, he was just in time to catch the Friday the 13th eruption of ash and pumice. Fed up, Perry took his revenge: "I went and got my pistol and 30.06 and emptied them at the mountain and called it every kind of name," he told a reporter.

©Gary Braasch

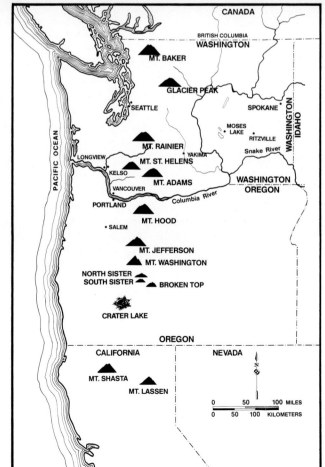

From the summit of South Sister, the Cascades form a phalanx trending northward that determines the weather, the plant systems and, in many ways, the identity of the Northwest. Once regarded as picturesque ornaments on the horizon, in the wake of St. Helens, people have become aware of the awesome power of those volcanoes as well. (Above from left to right, Middle Sister, St. Helens on the far horizon, Three Fingered Jack, Mount Jefferson, North Sister and Mount Hood.)

The volcanic phenomenon takes place on a scale so vast that man is dumbstruck in its presence, aftermath.

Maybe he missed. Judging by subsequent eruptions, he didn't kill it. Indeed, as much as we would like to, there's nothing much any of us can do about a volcano–except get out of its way. Perhaps it's this powerlessness to control, this extended lesson in nature's primacy, that Americans find hardest to accept about having a volcano as a neighbor.

The lesson may even be salutary. If technology encourages any expectation, it is that nature can be manipulated–dammed, dredged, diked back, sealed out or re-routed to suit our pleasure. This attitude is so deeply rooted that even those who oppose disturbing the wilderness share it. "I've learned how fragile beauty can be," one environmentalist has written about the Gifford Pinchot forest. "Nature–a mountain, a river, a waterfall, a forest–has no way of protecting itself. In today's world, they survive almost entirely on the good graces of men."

As a matter of fact, though, nature can be quite resourceful, and not a bit gentle. The volcano loosed the unkindest clearcut of all, taking down more trees in a matter of minutes than the timber companies would have felled over the next two years. Geologists have described the energy released by the May 18 blast in terms of the equivalent number of atomic bombs. In this respect, the difference between man and mountain is instructive. Nature regularly lets fly. And when the appointed moment comes, all our "good graces" are a matter of indifference.

What will the volcano do next? Judging by its history, Mount St. Helens–Fire Mountain–is capable of nearly anything in the future–of pouring liquid andesite lava down its flanks, of sending up great lava bombs that reshape themselves as they fall through the air, or of simply quieting down. The most likely course, though, is for the mountain to extrude a plug dome of sticky, dense dacite lava; blow the dome out in an eruption of ash and pumice; then grow another dome in a cycle that continues until the magma pool either sends up a more fluid product or spends itself.

The whole process could take a very long time–as with the 25 years of periodic activity in the 1800s. Alternatively, it could end quite soon. In an article authored by members of the Geophysics Program at the University of Washington in the magazine Nature, an explicit comparison has been made between St. Helens' behavior and the 1956 eruption of the volcano Bezymianny in the Soviet Union.

The similarities are remarkable in terms of pre-eruption seismic activity, time sequence and result. Bezymianny, like St. Helens, only rumbled a short while before ash eruptions began; and, like St. Helens, only a few more months went by before the climatic lateral blast was unleashed.

*(below) Queen Nephertite
perhaps? As the cloud of
destruction boiled upward on
May 18, it took on a new
aspect each minute in the
alembic of the imagination.*

*(overleaf) Midsummer dawn
silhouettes a climber at the
edge of the crater, reckless of
the danger, transfixed by the
glowing world naval.*

If the comparison continues to hold true, Northwesterners can take heart. Bezymianny's post-eruptive cool-down lasted only about six months, ending with the formation of a rounded, thousand-foot-high dacite dome inside the blast crater. St. Helens put up its first dacite dome only a few weeks after the May 18 blast. Geologists were encouraged – it signaled the beginning of a relatively stable phase, they thought. The dome itself looked like some great gray primal egg. As it grew, its skin cracked into an intricate network of fissures through which the coral glow of the magma could be glimpsed from the air. Although it looked small inside the giant mile-wide crater, the dome was as large as the Seattle Kingdome.

For Chuck Meissner, a Boise State University geology student, the lure proved irresistible. Claiming to represent the Washington Department of Emergency Services, he wangled a permit to make a helicopter survey of the mountain. Once in the air, Meissner convinced the helicopter pilot that it was okay to set down <u>inside the crater</u>. He wanted a piece of the rock.

The venture was a lesson in scale. Meissner had equipped himself only with a charcoal filtration mask. As he approached the dome, with its blocky surface of crusted lava, he realized it was giving off so much sulfur dioxide that all the oxygen around it was being displaced. Nonetheless, holding his breath (and looking much like a human fly on the edge of the monolith), he chipped away a sample from its margin, and, lungs bursting, dashed back to the helicopter.

Back in Portland, Meissner promptly found his access to the mountain permanently revoked. "What he did was illegal," says Dr. John Allen of the Portland State University Earth Sciences Department, who has chaired the permit-granting process for scientific access to the mountain. "However, we're mighty glad he gave us some of those samples for lab analysis."

*(opposite page)
Magma pressure from below had created a network of fissures on its surface. At the time, the dome measured 800 feet across by 200 feet high. The magma veins alone were several feet wide.*

A ring of vapor and gas escapes (bottom left) around the perimeter of an extruded dacite dome the size of the Seattle Kingdome. Geologists have determined that monitoring the plume of invisible gases given off by the volcano for levels of sulfur dioxide is the most accurate tool for predicting an imminent blow-out.

(below) Under a microscope, a cross section of the dome the size of a pin displays surprising geometric form and a translucent brilliance. The elongated pale yellow crystals are feldspar. The colorful grain at lower left is hypersthene, a type of pyroxene. The brown element is hornblende. These crystals are in a matrix of feldspar and glass.

©Gary Braasch

Ron Cronin

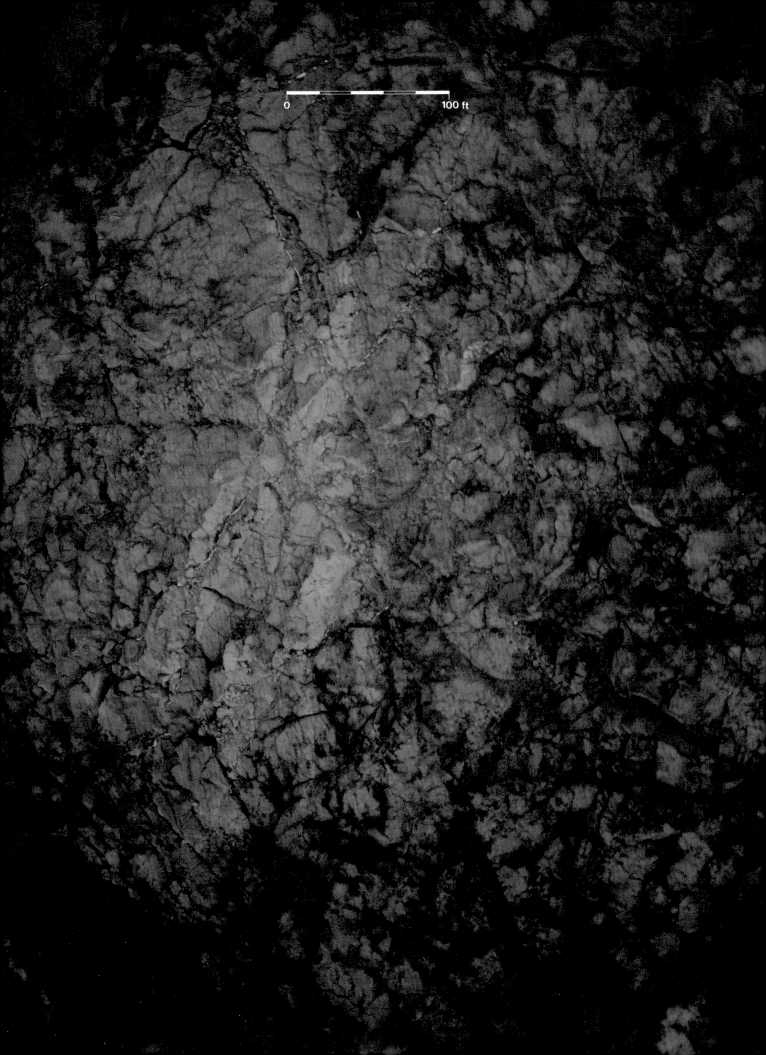

Michael Lloyd

James Mason

Doubtless, there was no question of gathering any more a couple of weeks later. By then, the dome had been blown to smithereens by a tremendous, spiraling eruption of ash that sent a mushroom cloud up to 50,000 feet. It happened on a clear day, fouling rush hour traffic in Portland as people stopped on bridges to witness the spectacle. By now the locals had become quite expert at gauging their reaction to the volcano's eruptions–they tuned in their radios and found out which way the wind was blowing. People no longer showed the euphoria of the initial phreatic bursts, or the depression after the big blast; they just climbed on top of their roofs and watched, awestruck. It was as though some kind of psychic adjustment had been made. The mountain was no longer performing or attacking–it was simply erupting.

French aviator and author Antoine de Saint Exupery has written that "when a man dies, an unknown world passes away." Death was certainly a part of the volcanic convulsion that rent Mount St. Helens–for 65 people, for some millions of wildlife.

But the volcanic processes speak to us of more than death. They point to an on-going cycle of succession in which the moment of destruction becomes the first step in the creation of the mountain's next avatar. Speak to us, that is, if we have ears to listen. Too often we don't. Our lifespans are a moment compared to the million years over which a Cascade peak is likely to remain active. The continental plates drift apart at a rate less rapid that the growth of a fingernail. And yet, geologists assure us, this drift accounts for the fires that burn under the world's volcanoes.

On July 22, the dome finally gave way, unloosing a tremendous column of ash that rose 50,000 feet in the air. Under the clear afternoon light, the ash billowed in dramatic chiarascuro, stopping traffic in the city as people left their cars to watch.

©Gary Braasch

Some have mourned the aftermath of the St. Helens eruption—the misshapen, tilted crown where once rose a splendid symmetrical summit; the blasted gray terrain in place of a climax Douglas fir forest.

Yet even as bits of the old St. Helens orbit the stratosphere, its successor is struggling to be born. As for devastation, in this landscape stripped to the sinew, an austere beauty may be found. How shall we look at it? From the air, the new dome is a gray broken mass swollen with heat and veined with magma. Under a microscope, a sliver of Chuck Meissner's dome specimen shakes with color and reveals an intricate geometry of crystalline form. The blast area is largely lifeless. But through cracks in the drying mud-flows, a pioneering line of grass sprouts skyward.

So it is that the living mountain touches us all—with a renewed sense of the unappeased cycle of nature and our place on the edge of an aborning continent. There is wonder in witnessing these events. And terror at nature's raw power. Ultimately, though, the transformation of St. Helens exhilirates us because, as St. Exupery knew, man dies. Mountains rise again.

Above, the July 22 eruption fades to the east in the lowering light.

©Gary Braasch

A week after the July 22 blowout, a view from the rim shows the prolapsed vent (right), concave below the floor of the crater, its rock sides heated to red hot incandescence. A little while later, following a relatively mild eruption, a new dome was extruded out of the vent. Thus, the cycle was closed, setting the stage for more volcanic activity that—this episode—may last for generations.

Robert Rodgers

Ron Cronin